GAILEARAÍ NÁISIÚNTA na hÉIREANN | NATIONAL GALLERY of IRELAND

DIARY 2019

NATIONAL
GALLERY of
IRELAND

Harry Clarke, *The Swineherd,* **1914–1915**

In Hans Christian Andersen's *Fairy Tales,* a prince disguises himself as a swineherd to woo an arrogant princess, who spurns his offering of a rose and a nightingale. She rejects his gifts, preferring to pay for toys that he creates with kisses. The prince, revealing his true identity, scorns her for her shallowness. Clarke depicts the prince elegantly attired in embellished royal attire. The glowing ultramarine blues in the background are a hallmark of Clarke's work.

TITLE PAGE Richard Cosway *Self-Portrait in Elizabethan Costume; A Lock of His Hair* **c.1790**

FRONT COVER AE [George William Russell] *Portrait of Iseult Gonne (Mrs Francis Stuart)*

BACK COVER Mainie Jellett, *The Virgin and Child,* **1936**

ENDPAPERS John Faulkner, *Inniskea Isle, Achill*

GAILEARAÍ NÁISIÚNTA^{na} hÉIREANN   NATIONAL GALLERY of IRELAND

www.nationalgallery.ie
Twitter @NGIreland
Facebook.com/nationalgalleryofireland

Gill Books
Hume Avenue, Park West, Dublin 12
www.gillbooks.ie

Gill Books is an imprint of M.H. Gill & Co.

© The National Gallery of Ireland 2018
978 0 7171 8145 2

Text researched and written by Sara Donaldson/NGI
Design by Tony Potter
Photography by Roy Hewson and Chris O'Toole/NGI

Print origination by Teapot Press Ltd
Printed in the EU

This book is typeset in Dax

2019

January • Eanáir
M	T	W	T	F	S	S
31	1	2	3	4	5	6
7	8	9	10	11	12	13
14	15	16	17	18	19	20
21	22	23	24	25	26	27
28	29	30	31	1	2	3

February • Feabhra
M	T	W	T	F	S	S
28	29	30	31	1	2	3
4	5	6	7	8	9	10
11	12	13	14	15	16	17
18	19	20	21	22	23	24
25	26	27	28	1	2	3

March • Márta
M	T	W	T	F	S	S
25	26	27	28	1	2	3
4	5	6	7	8	9	10
11	12	13	14	15	16	17
18	19	20	21	22	23	24
25	26	27	28	29	30	31

April • Aibreán
M	T	W	T	F	S	S
1	2	3	4	5	6	7
8	9	10	11	12	13	14
15	16	17	18	19	20	21
22	23	24	25	26	27	28
29	30	1	2	3	4	5

May • Bealtaine
M	T	W	T	F	S	S
29	30	1	2	3	4	5
6	7	8	9	10	11	12
13	14	15	16	17	18	19
20	21	22	23	24	25	26
27	28	29	30	31	1	2

June • Meitheamh
M	T	W	T	F	S	S
27	28	29	30	31	1	2
3	4	5	6	7	8	9
10	11	12	13	14	15	16
17	18	19	20	21	22	23
24	25	26	27	28	29	30

July • Iúil
M	T	W	T	F	S	S
1	2	3	4	5	6	7
8	9	10	11	12	13	14
15	16	17	18	19	20	21
22	23	24	25	26	27	28
29	30	31	1	2	3	4

August • Lúnasa
M	T	W	T	F	S	S
29	30	31	1	2	3	4
5	6	7	8	9	10	11
12	13	14	15	16	17	18
19	20	21	22	23	24	25
26	27	28	29	30	31	1

September • Meán Fómhair
M	T	W	T	F	S	S
26	27	28	29	30	31	1
2	3	4	5	6	7	8
9	10	11	12	13	14	15
16	17	18	19	20	21	22
23	24	25	26	27	28	29
30	1	2	3	4	5	6

October • Deireadh Fómhair
M	T	W	T	F	S	S
30	1	2	3	4	5	6
7	8	9	10	11	12	13
14	15	16	17	18	19	20
21	22	23	24	25	26	27
28	29	30	31	1	2	3

November • Samhain
M	T	W	T	F	S	S
28	29	30	31	1	2	3
4	5	6	7	8	9	10
11	12	13	14	15	16	17
18	19	20	21	22	23	24
25	26	27	28	29	30	1

December • Nollaig
M	T	W	T	F	S	S
25	26	27	28	29	30	1
2	3	4	5	6	7	8
9	10	11	12	13	14	15
16	17	18	19	20	21	22
23	24	25	26	27	28	29
30	31	1	2	3	4	5

2020

January • Eanáir
M	T	W	T	F	S	S
30	31	1	2	3	4	5
6	7	8	9	10	11	12
13	14	15	16	17	18	19
20	21	22	23	24	25	26
27	28	29	30	31	1	2

February • Feabhra
M	T	W	T	F	S	S
27	28	29	30	31	1	2
3	4	5	6	7	8	9
10	11	12	13	14	15	16
17	18	19	20	21	22	23
24	25	26	27	28	29	1

March • Márta
M	T	W	T	F	S	S
24	25	26	27	28	29	1
2	3	4	5	6	7	8
9	10	11	12	13	14	15
16	17	18	19	20	21	22
23	24	25	26	27	28	29
30	31	1	2	3	4	5

April • Aibreán
M	T	W	T	F	S	S
30	31	1	2	3	4	5
6	7	8	9	10	11	12
13	14	15	16	17	18	19
20	21	22	23	24	25	26
27	28	29	30	1	2	3

May • Bealtaine
M	T	W	T	F	S	S
27	28	29	30	1	2	3
4	5	6	7	8	9	10
11	12	13	14	15	16	17
18	19	20	21	22	23	24
25	26	27	28	29	30	31

June • Meitheamh
M	T	W	T	F	S	S
1	2	3	4	5	6	7
8	9	10	11	12	13	14
15	16	17	18	19	20	21
22	23	24	25	26	27	28
29	30	1	2	3	4	5

July • Iúil
M	T	W	T	F	S	S
29	30	1	2	3	4	5
6	7	8	9	10	11	12
13	14	15	16	17	18	19
20	21	22	23	24	25	26
27	28	29	30	31	1	2

August • Lúnasa
M	T	W	T	F	S	S
27	28	29	30	31	1	2
3	4	5	6	7	8	9
10	11	12	13	14	15	16
17	18	19	20	21	22	23
24	25	26	27	28	29	30
31	1	2	3	4	5	6

September • Meán Fómhair
M	T	W	T	F	S	S
31	1	2	3	4	5	6
7	8	9	10	11	12	13
14	15	16	17	18	19	20
21	22	23	24	25	26	27
28	29	30	1	2	3	4

October • Deireadh Fómhair
M	T	W	T	F	S	S
28	29	30	1	2	3	4
5	6	7	8	9	10	11
12	13	14	15	16	17	18
19	20	21	22	23	24	25
26	27	28	29	30	31	1

November • Samhain
M	T	W	T	F	S	S
26	27	28	29	30	31	1
2	3	4	5	6	7	8
9	10	11	12	13	14	15
16	17	18	19	20	21	22
23	24	25	26	27	28	29
30	1	2	3	4	5	6

December • Nollaig
M	T	W	T	F	S	S
30	1	2	3	4	5	6
7	8	9	10	11	12	13
14	15	16	17	18	19	20
21	22	23	24	25	26	27
28	29	30	31	1	2	3

The National Gallery of Ireland Diary for 2019 scratches at the surface to reveal some of the many layers represented in our collections. The presence of some perennial favourites, such as *The Meeting on the Turret Stairs*, or our beautiful Metsu paintings, is enriched by new arrivals. These include the recent portrait of Graham Norton, which has proved enormously popular with visitors since going up on display. The Irish collection as a whole has been given renewed prominence in the fine, pale-grey galleries of the Milltown wing. As this is the main route for members of the public to traverse between the Clare Street and Merrion Square entrances, the presence of our Irish works has rarely been more eye-catching.

Many, particularly paintings and works on paper from the 19th and early 20th centuries, are featured prominently in this 2019 diary. Some, such as images by Roderic O'Conor, remind us of the 2018 summer exhibition of his Pont-Aven period works held at the Gallery. The show put these into a context of works by illustrious and lesser-known artists, ranging from Van Gogh to Cuno Amiet. This era in art development had profound consequences on the following century. In this diary, however, there is an emphasis on more traditional Irish landscape painting and portraiture of the period. Those unfolding and more revolutionary changes in rich colours and expressive brushwork can be seen, by contrast, in the paintings by Gabriele Münter, one of several works by prominent women artists, and Chaïm Soutine.

The Gallery has now been reopened for more than a year. Our visitors have marvelled at the new collection displays, which show expansively the evolution of art over the past centuries. The Gallery's collection has depth as well as breadth. Visitors can track the major developments in international and Irish art over several centuries. Much of this richness is contained within the pages of this diary, giving visual stimulation and great pleasure as art lovers leaf through these pages, making appointments and noting the days they will come to see an exhibition, hear a talk, take part in an event or sit quietly and contemplate a work with a special meaning for them.

Our future plans, for finishing the Master Development Plan and creating new galleries, new facilities for education, the library and archive, and a proper home for our superb conservation department, are in active development. We will build on the successes of the past year to finish the most major building works we have ever undertaken. We do so in order to give the great art illustrated in these pages the home it merits.

Sean Rainbird, Director, NGI

Gareth Reid, *Graham Norton (b.1963), Broadcaster, Comedian, Actor, Writer,* **2017**

Cork-raised Norton moved to London and studied at the Central School of Speech and Drama. From stand-up comedy he gravitated towards radio and television, featuring on panel and quiz shows. A winner of five BAFTA TV awards, Norton is best known as a television chat show host, most recently of *The Graham Norton Show* on the BBC. In 2016, his debut novel, *Holding,* won the Popular Fiction Book of the Year at the Bord Gáis Irish Book Awards. Glasgow-based Gareth Reid was commissioned to paint this portrait as the winner of Sky Arts *Portrait Artist of the Year 2017*.

31 Monday · Luan
New Year's Eve

1 Tuesday · Máirt
New Year's Day

2019 January · Eanáir

2 Wednesday · Céadaoin

3 Thursday · Déardaoin

4 Friday · Aoine

5 Saturday · Satharn

6 Sunday · Domhnach

Joseph Mallord William Turner, *A Ship Against the Mew Stone, at the entrance to Plymouth Sound,* **c.1814**

In summer 1813 Turner travelled along the southern coast of England, making sketches and observations which he later developed into watercolours. The Mew Stone, lying off shore at Wembury Bay, is a dramatic natural feature responsible for claiming many lives. A small ship lurches against the tossing sea, but is not in danger, having reefed its top sails, thus lowering its centre of gravity. Turner accurately depicts the white crests of the waves being blown by the wind, the rigging of the labouring ship, the clouds highlighted by a shaft of sunlight and the gannets with their black wing tips.

M	T	W	T	F	S	S
31	1	2	3	4	5	6
7	8	9	10	11	12	13
14	15	16	17	18	19	20
21	22	23	24	25	26	27
28	29	30	31	1	2	3

January · Eanáir
Week 2 · Seachtain 2

7 Monday · Luan

8 Tuesday · Máirt

9 Wednesday · Céadaoin

10 Thursday · Déardaoin

11 Friday · Aoine

12 Saturday · Satharn

13 Sunday · Domhnach

Christian Adolf Schreyer, *Arab Horsemen,* **1865/1885**

Schreyer's visits to Syria, Egypt and Algeria informed his colourful scenes, which catered to the French market for Orientalist painting. He made detailed studies of horses and bridles and prided himself on their accuracy, while keeping his locations nondescript. This is a characteristic example of Schreyer's horsemen who, having perhaps watered their animals, seem ready to set out again. The rider in the centre, astride his white steed, may be the leader. He sits back in his saddle with confidence, anchoring the composition, while around him the other riders attend to their frisky horses.

M	T	W	T	F	S	S
31	1	2	3	4	5	6
7	8	9	10	11	12	13
14	15	16	17	18	19	20
21	22	23	24	25	26	27
28	29	30	31	1	2	3

January · Eanáir
Week 3 · Seachtain 3

14 Monday · Luan

15 Tuesday · Máirt

16 Wednesday · Céadaoin

17 Thursday · Déardaoin

18 Friday · Aoine

19 Saturday · Satharn

20 Sunday · Domhnach

Howard Helmick, *News of the Land League,* **1881**

This American artist's paintings of rural Ireland shed light on a range of topical and political issues that Irish painters often avoided as controversial. Here, a group of country folk listen to their literate friend reading from a newspaper. Behind them, a man points out a poster, headed with the words 'Land League' to his companion, who scratches his head in puzzlement. The Land League, founded by Michael Davitt in 1879, aimed to protect tenants from eviction and rack-renting. In 1881 Gladstone's Land Act was passed in response to demands for fair rent, fixity of tenure and free sale of holdings.

M	T	W	T	F	S	S
31	1	2	3	4	5	6
7	8	9	10	11	12	13
14	15	16	17	18	19	20
21	22	23	24	25	26	27
28	29	30	31	1	2	3

21 Monday • Luan

22 Tuesday • Máirt

23 Wednesday • Céadaoin

24 Thursday • Déardaoin

25 Friday • Aoine

26 Saturday • Satharn

27 Sunday • Domhnach

Ascribed to Frans Hals, or Studio of Hals, *A Fisherboy,* **c.1630**

During the 1630s, Hals visited Scheveningen, a coastal resort on the North Sea near The Hague, where he painted a series of pictures of fisher children against sand dunes and sea where the distinction between portraiture and genre is blurred. Paintings of fisherfolk were also made by Hals's closer followers and studio members. This boy proudly displays a dripping fish, his mouth open as if crying out to buyers, revealing an irregular line of teeth. His wicker basket ripples with colour and picks up the red of his cap and shirt sleeves. The broad brushwork lends the work a sense of vivacity.

M	T	W	T	F	S	S
31	1	2	3	4	5	6
7	8	9	10	11	12	13
14	15	16	17	18	19	20
21	22	23	24	25	26	27
28	29	30	31	1	2	3

28 Monday • Luan

29 Tuesday • Máirt

30 Wednesday • Céadaoin

31 Thursday • Déardaoin

1 Friday • Aoine

February • Feabhra

2 Saturday • Satharn

3 Sunday • Domhnach

Robert Ponsonby Staples, *On the Beach, Broadstairs, Kent,* **1899**

In this delightful painting, we see a familiar day at the seaside. Blustery weather has not deterred people from playing on the beach. A young girl walks her dog, clutching her straw hat with one hand to keep it in place. Nearby, young boys are building sandcastles, while others brave the rolling waves. The sketchiness of Staples' technique perfectly captures the atmosphere. This painting may be the one exhibited as *Our Holiday* in 1901.

M	T	W	T	F	S	S
31	1	2	3	4	5	6
7	8	9	10	11	12	13
14	15	16	17	18	19	20
21	22	23	24	25	26	27
28	29	30	31	1	2	3

4 Monday · Luan

5 Tuesday · Máirt

6 Wednesday · Céadaoin

7 Thursday · Déardaoin

8 Friday · Aoine

9 Saturday · Satharn

10 Sunday · Domhnach

Sarah Cecilia Harrison, *Self-Portrait,* **late 19th/early 20th century**

Born in County Down, Harrison became one of Ireland's foremost portrait painters, notable for her high level of realism and precise brushwork. Her self-portraits are painted in the academic tradition. Sarah was an early campaigner for the establishment of a museum of modern art in Dublin, a cause supported by Hugh Lane, her close friend. In 1912 she became the first woman to be elected to Dublin City Council, and was a revolutionary councillor, fighting for the rights of tenants, the conditions of the poor and the unemployed. A suffragette, at over six feet tall, she cut quite a figure.

M	T	W	T	F	S	S
28	29	30	31	1	2	3
4	5	6	7	8	9	10
11	12	13	14	15	16	17
18	19	20	21	22	23	24
25	26	27	28	1	2	3

February · Feabhra
Week 7 · Seachtain 7

11 Monday · Luan

12 Tuesday · Máirt

13 Wednesday · Céadaoin

14 Thursday · Déardaoin
St Valentine's Day

15 Friday · Aoine

16 Saturday · Satharn

17 Sunday · Domhnach

Frederic William Burton, *Hellelil and Hildebrand, the Meeting on the Turret Stairs,* **1864**

The medieval Danish ballad *Helelill and Hildebrand* tells of Hellelil's love for her bodyguard Hildebrand, whose death is ordered by her angered father. Burton depicts the moment of the couple's final meeting, before Hildebrand goes to meet his death. Their averted eyes and tender embrace are poignant yet understated, implying the inevitable tragedy to follow. Burton's interest in the art and legend of the Middle Ages was shared with the English Pre-Raphaelite artists, whom he knew in London. This watercolour resembles an oil painting due to his meticulous technique, depth of colour and use of opaque gouache to highlight details.

M	T	W	T	F	S	S
28	29	30	31	1	2	3
4	5	6	7	8	9	10
11	12	13	14	15	16	17
18	19	20	21	22	23	24
25	26	27	28	1	2	3

18 Monday · Luan

19 Tuesday · Máirt

20 Wednesday · Céadaoin

21 Thursday · Déardaoin

22 Friday · Aoine

23 Saturday · Satharn

24 Sunday · Domhnach

Richard Rothwell, *Calisto,* **c.1840**
Born in Athlone, Rothwell established a successful portrait practice in London, where his work was admired
by the English painters Edwin Landseer and Thomas Lawrence, who prized the richness of his palette and
compared his skill in painting flesh to that of the Old Masters. In a letter to George Mulvany, first Director
of the National Gallery of Ireland, Rothwell wrote that he considered this painting, the subject of which is
derived from classical mythology, his finest picture, declaring that he had worked on it until it 'arrived at
that state of perfection on which my judgement cannot add another touch'.

M	T	W	T	F	S	S
28	29	30	31	1	2	3
4	5	6	7	8	9	10
11	12	13	14	15	16	17
18	19	20	21	22	23	24
25	26	27	28	1	2	3

25 Monday · Luan

26 Tuesday · Máirt

27 Wednesday · Céadaoin

28 Thursday · Déardaoin

1 Friday · Aoine   March · Márta

2 Saturday · Satharn

3 Sunday · Domhnach

Howard Helmick, *The Bookworm,* **19th century**

Ohio-born artist Howard Helmick moved to London from where he travelled to Ireland throughout the 1870s and 1880s, at one stage living in Dangan Cottage, Galway. An accomplished genre painter, he excelled in his depiction of Irish subjects, showing a real understanding of rural life and customs. He was also interested in literacy and education, both recurring themes in his work, evident in this interior of a middle-aged scholar poring over his leather-bound books. The location of this scene is not necessarily Irish, however, and Helmick used the same fine table and chairs in another work, *A Fine Vintage*.

M	T	W	T	F	S	S
28	29	30	31	1	2	3
4	5	6	7	8	9	10
11	12	13	14	15	16	17
18	19	20	21	22	23	24
25	26	27	28	1	2	3

H. Helmi

4 Monday · Luan

5 Tuesday · Máirt

6 Wednesday · Céadaoin

7 Thursday · Déardaoin

8 Friday · Aoine
International Women's Day

9 Saturday · Satharn

10 Sunday · Domhnach

Gabriele Münter, *Girl with a Red Ribbon,* **1908**

In 1908, the year she painted this picture, Münter settled in the village of Murnau, southern Bavaria, with her partner Wassily Kandinsky. Her work developed quickly at a time when she and Kandinsky were becoming leading members of the Expressionist movement. The girl depicted here wears a high-collared white blouse and a red ribbon in her hair. The green, red, purple and pink hues in her face reveal the influence of Van Gogh and Matisse. Other sources of inspiration are German folk art and Bavarian glass painting, the latter evident in the flat background colours separated by heavy, dark lines.

M	T	W	T	F	S	S
25	26	27	28	1	2	3
4	5	6	7	8	9	10
11	12	13	14	15	16	17
18	19	20	21	22	23	24
25	26	27	28	29	30	31

11 Monday • Luan

12 Tuesday • Máirt

13 Wednesday • Céadaoin

14 Thursday • Déardaoin

15 Friday • Aoine

16 Saturday • Satharn

17 Sunday • Domhnach
St Patrick's Day

John Lavery, *Saint Patrick's Purgatory, Lough Derg,* **1929**
Station Island, Lough Derg, County Donegal, the traditional location of Saint Patrick's purgatory, soon became associated with him, attracting pilgrims since the Middle Ages. In August 1929, Lavery travelled there for artistic rather than religious purposes and created preparatory sketches for the final painting (held at Dublin City Gallery the Hugh Lane). Lavery was disappointed by the pilgrims he encountered, who were not 'picturesque' peasants, but 'everyday types one would see in the streets of Belfast or Dublin', and by the good weather during his stay, which he feared would make his pictures of Lough Derg 'look like a crowded summer resort'.

M	T	W	T	F	S	S
25	26	27	28	1	2	3
4	5	6	7	8	9	10
11	12	13	14	15	16	17
18	19	20	21	22	23	24
25	26	27	28	29	30	31

SAINT PATRICK'S PURGATORY
WITH MANY COMPLIMENTS
FROM JOHN LAVERY
9 APRIL 1932
TO MONSIGNORE
VANCE.

18 Monday • Luan

Bank Holiday

19 Tuesday • Máirt

20 Wednesday • Céadaoin

21 Thursday • Déardaoin

22 Friday • Aoine

23 Saturday • Satharn

24 Sunday • Domhnach

Roderic O'Conor, *Bretonne,* **c.1903–1904**

O'Conor spent over a decade in Pont Aven, regularly painting the villagers in traditional Breton costume and capturing their quiet dignity. This girl modelled for three paintings in which O'Conor observed her with detachment. Her reserved, sullen, even haughty expression lends the portrait an air of aloofness, bordering on suspicion. He has linked her face to the background through the striped shadow on the side of her cheek. These dazzling stripes of complementary red and green betray the influence of the Post-Impressionists Gauguin and van Gogh on the Irish artist.

M	T	W	T	F	S	S
25	26	27	28	1	2	3
4	5	6	7	8	9	10
11	12	13	14	15	16	17
18	19	20	21	22	23	24
25	26	27	28	29	30	31

25 Monday · Luan

26 Tuesday · Máirt

27 Wednesday · Céadaoin

28 Thursday · Déardaoin

29 Friday · Aoine

30 Saturday · Satharn

31 Sunday · Domhnach
Mothering Sunday

Caravaggio (Michelangelo Merisi) *The Taking of Christ,* **1602**
This powerful work was painted at the height of Caravaggio's fame, and the theatrical light and realistically observed figures are representative of his mature style. The drama reaches an emotional pitch as Judas kisses and identifies Christ, who does not resist his arrest by the soldiers, menacingly clad in shining black armour. The fleeing disciple on the left is St John the Evangelist, whose face is united with those of Jesus and Judas by moonlight.

M	T	W	T	F	S	S
25	26	27	28	1	2	3
4	5	6	7	8	9	10
11	12	13	14	15	16	17
18	19	20	21	22	23	24
25	26	27	28	29	30	31

April · Aibreán
Week 14 · Seachtain 14

1 Monday · Luan

2 Tuesday · Máirt

3 Wednesday · Céadaoin

4 Thursday · Déardaoin

5 Friday · Aoine

6 Saturday · Satharn

7 Sunday · Domhnach

Colin Middleton, *Landscape in May, Carnmoney,* **1943**

This view of a quiet corner of County Antrim takes a high vantage point of these rolling hills, fields, trees, woods and grassy knolls. A ploughed field divides the foreground and background, while contrasting areas of light and dark suggest distance. This landscape is representative of Middleton's simpler work. Born in Belfast, the son of a landscape painter and damask designer, Colin worked in his father's firm for 20 years before taking up painting full-time. He settled in County Down and later in County Antrim, where his love of landscape was rekindled by the distinctive light, local configurations and vegetation there.

M	T	W	T	F	S	S
1	2	3	4	5	6	7
8	9	10	11	12	13	14
15	16	17	18	19	20	21
22	23	24	25	26	27	28
29	30	1	2	3	4	5

8 Monday · Luan

9 Tuesday · Máirt

10 Wednesday · Céadaoin

11 Thursday · Déardaoin

12 Friday · Aoine

13 Saturday · Satharn

14 Sunday · Domhnach

William Evans of Eton, *Interior with a Woman Spinning, a Pot on a Open Fire,* **1838**

In the 1830s Evans made two tours of Connemara and Galway city. In 1835, Henry D. Inglis had published a guidebook, *A Journey Throughout Ireland, During the Spring, Summer and Autumn of 1834,* providing much detail on the life and customs of the Gaelic-speaking people of Mayo and Galway. In the Claddagh, Inglis was impressed by the industry of the inhabitants: 'I looked into hundreds of cabins, and there was scarcely one in which I did not see females busily engaged in spinning, making or mending nets ... .' Evans's interiors such as this were probably inspired by Inglis's descriptions.

M	T	W	T	F	S	S
1	2	3	4	5	6	7
8	9	10	11	12	13	14
15	16	17	18	19	20	21
22	23	24	25	26	27	28
29	30	1	2	3	4	5

April · Aibreán
Week 16 · Seachtain 16

15 Monday · Luan

16 Tuesday · Máirt

17 Wednesday · Céadaoin

18 Thursday · Déardaoin

19 Friday · Aoine
Good Friday

20 Saturday · Satharn

21 Sunday · Domhnach
Easter

Stanley Royle, *The Goose Girl,* **c.1921**

This colourful painting belongs to a series of pictures with woodland settings made by Royle around his native Sheffield in the years between 1913 and 1923. His wife Lily posed as the girl moving her geese through a bluebell wood in spring. Her lack of expression and the frieze-like composition contribute to the sense of a frozen moment captured in time. The purple and green hues of the bluebell wood complement the girl's orange dress, on which sunlight is reflected. The vivid palette and the thick application of paint reveal the influence of the French Impressionists' technique on this English artist.

M	T	W	T	F	S	S
1	2	3	4	5	6	7
8	9	10	11	12	13	14
15	16	17	18	19	20	21
22	23	24	25	26	27	28
29	30	1	2	3	4	5

April · Aibreán
Week 17 · Seachtain 17

22 Monday · Luan
Easter Monday

23 Tuesday · Máirt

24 Wednesday · Céadaoin

25 Thursday · Déardaoin

26 Friday · Aoine

27 Saturday · Satharn

28 Sunday · Domhnach

Bernardo Strozzi, *Allegory of Summer and Spring,* **late 1630s**

These female figures are personifications of summer, on the left, and spring, on the right, holding the attributes of their respective seasons. Summer carries a cornucopia of fruits and has sprigs of corn in her hair, while Spring holds various flowers in her hands and more blossoms decorate her hair. Strozzi hailed from Genoa, later settling in Venice, where fruit and corn both ripen in summer, much earlier in the year than in Britain and Ireland. This painting dates from the last period of his career, when Strozzi's use of delicate Venetian colouring and light and rich impasto became looser.

M	T	W	T	F	S	S
1	2	3	4	5	6	7
8	9	10	11	12	13	14
15	16	17	18	19	20	21
22	23	24	25	26	27	28
29	30	1	2	3	4	5

29 Monday · Luan

30 Tuesday · Máirt

1 Wednesday · Céadaoin   May · Bealtaine

2 Thursday · Déardaoin

3 Friday · Aoine

4 Saturday · Satharn

5 Sunday · Domhnach

After Jean-Baptiste Greuze, *The Capuchin Doll,* **18th century**

Greuze won popularity in France with his expressive paintings of children and young girls, some full of naïve grace, others rather sentimental. This fair-haired child wears a white cap with blue ribbon and leans against a ledge, holding a doll in the figure of a Capuchin monk. Greuze exhibited the original painting at the Paris Salon of 1765. His works were engraved and copied by numerous artists during his own lifetime and the present painting may be a copy after the original. It nevertheless illustrates how Greuze introduced a Dutch-influenced realism into French genre painting of the 18th century.

M	T	W	T	F	S	S
1	2	3	4	5	6	7
8	9	10	11	12	13	14
15	16	17	18	19	20	21
22	23	24	25	26	27	28
29	30	1	2	3	4	5

6 Monday · Luan
Bank Holiday (RoI and NI)

7 Tuesday · Máirt

8 Wednesday · Céadaoin

9 Thursday · Déardaoin

10 Friday · Aoine

11 Saturday · Satharn

12 Sunday · Domhnach

John Butler Yeats, *Pippa Passes,* **1870–1872**

In 1870 Yeats was commissioned to make a drawing of Pippa from Robert Browning's series of narrative poems, *Bless and Pomegranates. Pippa Passes,* the first in the series, tells of a girl from the silk mills in Asolo who passes through the lives of others, imagining herself into their situations and so influencing them. Yeats depicts Pippa wandering through a wood in early morning. Her hair falls away from her thrown-back head, her mouth opens slightly, and her eyes gaze out abstractedly. Her white sleeves, pink sash, apron and blue skirt sway as she seems to float through the forest.

M	T	W	T	F	S	S
29	30	1	2	3	4	5
6	7	8	9	10	11	12
13	14	15	16	17	18	19
20	21	22	23	24	25	26
27	28	29	30	31	1	2

13 Monday • Luan

14 Tuesday • Máirt

15 Wednesday • Céadaoin

16 Thursday • Déardaoin

17 Friday • Aoine

18 Saturday • Satharn

19 Sunday • Domhnach

Melchior de Hondecoeter, *Poultry,* **1660s–1690s**
The birds at the near edge of a pond include a domestic drake, a drake teal, a drake wigeon and ducklings.
On the far side of the water are a domestic crested cock, hen and chicks, and a duckling. Domesticated
and wild birds are shown together, as some wild birds were at that time kept captive or pinioned as
ornamental birds. The picture's setting enhances the sense of realism, as do the birds' lively movements.
De Hondecoeter trained with his father and his uncle, Jan Baptist Weenix. He specialised in bird pictures
and had many imitators during his long career.

M	T	W	T	F	S	S
29	30	1	2	3	4	5
6	7	8	9	10	11	12
13	14	15	16	17	18	19
20	21	22	23	24	25	26
27	28	29	30	31	1	2

May · Bealtaine
Week 21 · Seachtain 21

20 Monday · Luan

21 Tuesday · Máirt

22 Wednesday · Céadaoin

23 Thursday · Déardaoin

24 Friday · Aoine

25 Saturday · Satharn

26 Sunday · Domhnach

Vincent Van Gogh, *Rooftops in Paris,* **1886**

Vincent Van Gogh travelled from his native Holland to Paris in early 1886, where he rented an apartment
with his brother Theo on the Rue Lepic near Montmartre. This bohemian district of Paris afforded panoramic
views of the city, and from his window, Vincent painted four views of the rooftops. This painting, one of the
aforementioned series, shows the city centre extending south. The thick application of paint evokes a cloudy,
overcast sky.

M	T	W	T	F	S	S
29	30	1	2	3	4	5
6	7	8	9	10	11	12
13	14	15	16	17	18	19
20	21	22	23	24	25	26
27	28	29	30	31	1	2

May • Bealtaine
Week 22 • Seachtain 22

27 Monday • Luan

28 Tuesday • Máirt

29 Wednesday • Céadaoin

30 Thursday • Déardaoin

31 Friday • Aoine

1 Saturday • Satharn   June • Meitheamh

2 Sunday • Domhnach

Richard Rothwell, *A Study from Nature – Glendalough – Guides to the Churches on the Look-out for Tourists' Baskets,* **19th century**

Amidst foxgloves and other wild flowers, a boy and girl sit on a grassy bank, waiting expectantly for potential customers whom they may plan to intercept with an offer of a guided tour of this famous historical site, a popular tourist destination in the 19th century, as now. Behind them, the tall blue hills of Glendalough, the uncapped round tower and the lake blend with the cloudy sky. In 1858 Rothwell exhibited *Vale of Glendalough* at the British Institution, which might correspond to this work. His images of children highlight their innocence while avoiding the cloying sentimentality of many Victorian paintings.

M	T	W	T	F	S	S
29	30	1	2	3	4	5
6	7	8	9	10	11	12
13	14	15	16	17	18	19
20	21	22	23	24	25	26
27	28	29	30	31	1	2

June • Meitheamh
Week 23 • Seachtain 23

3 Monday • Luan
Bank Holiday (RoI)

4 Tuesday • Máirt

5 Wednesday • Céadaoin

6 Thursday • Déardaoin

7 Friday • Aoine

8 Saturday • Satharn

9 Sunday • Domhnach

James Humbert Craig, *Cushendun in June,* **20th century**
Craig painted scenic parts of Counties Antrim and Down, including Cushendun, a picturesque village on the Antrim coast at the mouth of the River Dun. The cottages depicted here were commissioned by Lord Cushendun and designed by the architect Clough Williams-Ellis. They became known as Maud Cottages after Maud Bolitho, the Cornish-born wife of Lord Cushendun, and were built in the Cornish style with whitewashed walls, slate-hung roofs and tall chimneys. Craig had a cottage in the village and painted there until his death. This area is now preserved by the National Trust.

M	T	W	T	F	S	S
27	28	29	30	31	1	2
3	4	5	6	7	8	9
10	11	12	13	14	15	16
17	18	19	20	21	22	23
24	25	26	27	28	29	30

10 Monday · Luan

11 Tuesday · Máirt

12 Wednesday · Céadaoin

13 Thursday · Déardaoin

14 Friday · Aoine

15 Saturday · Satharn

16 Sunday · Domhnach

William John Leech, *A Convent Garden, Brittany,* **c.1913**

During his early career Leech painted *en plein air* in Concarneau, Brittany. In 1904 he had convalesced from typhoid fever in a local hospital and convent run by the Sisters of the Holy Ghost, whose garden is the setting for this luminous picture. The main figure is Elizabeth Saurine, Leech's first wife, posing as a novice of the Soeurs du Saint-Esprit. She glides past the viewer wearing the traditional costume of Breton novices on the day they took their final vows. Her habit's white shades reflect the colours of the leaves and petals of the lilies, themselves symbolic of purity.

M	T	W	T	F	S	S
27	28	29	30	31	1	2
3	4	5	6	7	8	9
10	11	12	13	14	15	16
17	18	19	20	21	22	23
24	25	26	27	28	29	30

June • Meitheamh
Week 25 • Seachtain 25

17 Monday • Luan

18 Tuesday • Máirt

19 Wednesday • Céadaoin

20 Thursday • Déardaoin

21 Friday • Aoine

22 Saturday • Satharn

23 Sunday • Domhnach

William Orpen, *Looking at the Sea,* **1912**

Orpen holidayed on Howth Head every summer from 1909 until the outbreak of the First World War. He rented a house called The Cliffs with spectacular views of Dublin Bay. His children recalled how, during these holidays, they were required to pose for their father, 'but only an hour at a time then a dash along the cliffs for a bathe – golden days'. Orpen depicts himself and his wife Grace relaxing under the tent they erected as a wind shelter on the spot where they liked to picnic. The mood of sunlit tranquillity is reflected in Orpen's lightness of touch.

M	T	W	T	F	S	S
27	28	29	30	31	1	2
3	4	5	6	7	8	9
10	11	12	13	14	15	16
17	18	19	20	21	22	23
24	25	26	27	28	29	30

June · Meitheamh
Week 26 · Seachtain 26

24 Monday · Luan

25 Tuesday · Máirt

26 Wednesday · Céadaoin

27 Thursday · Déardaoin

28 Friday · Aoine

29 Saturday · Satharn

30 Sunday · Domhnach

Chaïm Soutine, *Landscape with Flight of Stairs,* **c.1922**

Soutine painted a series of landscapes at Céret in the French Pyrenees in 1919-1922, and at Cagnes-sur-Mer on the Côte d'Azur in the foothills of the Alpes Maritimes in 1922-1923. This work may belong to the latter series and is one of several views of hilltop villages with stepped streets that are regarded as Soutine's most Expressionist works. A solitary man descends the steps but leans over to the left, appearing unstable, while cypress trees strain against the edges of the canvas. The low vantage point creates a sensation of one being immersed in this turbulent scene, charged with movement.

M	T	W	T	F	S	S
27	28	29	30	31	1	2
3	4	5	6	7	8	9
10	11	12	13	14	15	16
17	18	19	20	21	22	23
24	25	26	27	28	29	30

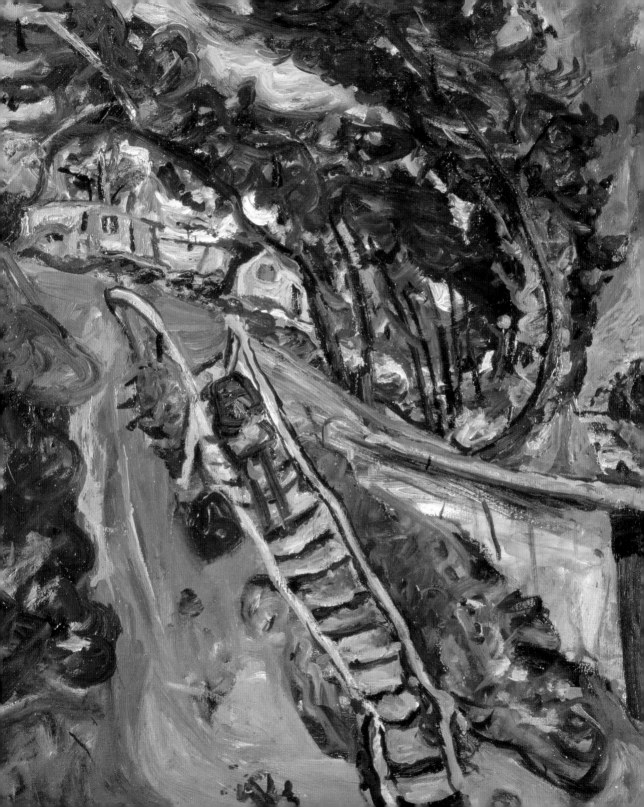

July · Iúil
Week 27 · Seachtain 27

1 Monday · Luan

2 Tuesday · Máirt

3 Wednesday · Céadaoin

4 Thursday · Déardaoin

5 Friday · Aoine

6 Saturday · Satharn

7 Sunday · Domhnach

Mary Swanzy, *Clown by Candlelight,* **1942–1943**

The Second World War profoundly affected Swanzy, whose house in London was bombed. She moved back to Dublin, her art becoming tinged with foreboding as she reflected on the physical ravages of war as well as its effect on the psyche. An ominous note dominates this painting, apparent in the melancholy expression of the clown, a lonely, almost tragic figure who cups his face in his hands, gazing reflectively at a candle. Its flame may symbolise the austere circumstances in which many people found themselves during the war, or may be a metaphor for Swanzy's feelings of uncertainty and hope.

M	T	W	T	F	S	S
1	2	3	4	5	6	7
8	9	10	11	12	13	14
15	16	17	18	19	20	21
22	23	24	25	26	27	28
29	30	31	1	2	3	4

8 Monday · Luan

9 Tuesday · Máirt

10 Wednesday · Céadaoin

11 Thursday · Déardaoin

12 Friday · Aoine

13 Saturday · Satharn

14 Sunday · Domhnach

William Crozier, *The Re-planting,* **2008**

In 2005 Graphic Studio Dublin approached the National Gallery of Ireland with an idea for *Revelation,* an exhibition of prints by contemporary artists, who were encouraged to search the Gallery's collection for inspiration. Crozier's carborundum print for the *Revelation* exhibition was inspired by Claude Lorrain's painting *Juno Confiding Io to the Care of Argus.* Crozier was born in Glasgow to Irish parents, and his work is deeply earth-bound. He treated the landscape in a vividly coloured, strongly structured approach to convey emotional intensity. An Irish citizen, he worked regularly in West Cork until his death in 2011.

M	T	W	T	F	S	S
1	2	3	4	5	6	7
8	9	10	11	12	13	14
15	16	17	18	19	20	21
22	23	24	25	26	27	28
29	30	31	1	2	3	4

July · Iúil
Week 29 · Seachtain 29

15 Monday · Luan

16 Tuesday · Máirt

17 Wednesday · Céadaoin

18 Thursday · Déardaoin

19 Friday · Aoine

20 Saturday · Satharn

21 Sunday · Domhnach

Walter Frederick Osborne, *Dublin Streets: A Vendor of Books,* **1889**

A bookseller plies his trade as customers crowd around his stall, watched by a flower seller holding a baby, while a barefoot girl attempts to charm the gentlemen perusing books into buying daffodils. The location is Aston Quay in Dublin, a popular spot among street hawkers and stall holders for generations. A barge and skiff on the river are evidence of the Liffey's status as a working river, while the view eastwards includes the recently renamed O'Connell Bridge, and James Gandon's Custom House. Osborne's celebration of urban subjects and his acknowledgement of inner-city Dublin hardships are both evident here.

M	T	W	T	F	S	S
1	2	3	4	5	6	7
8	9	10	11	12	13	14
15	16	17	18	19	20	21
22	23	24	25	26	27	28
29	30	31	1	2	3	4

22 Monday · Luan

23 Tuesday · Máirt

24 Wednesday · Céadaoin

25 Thursday · Déardaoin

26 Friday · Aoine

27 Saturday · Satharn

28 Sunday · Domhnach

William Orpen, *The Wash House,* **1905**

The model for this painting was Lottie Stafford, a cockney washerwoman who lived and worked in Paradise Walk, a slum neighbourhood in Chelsea, East London. She became one of William Orpen's favourite models. Here, she is captured pausing momentarily and looking up from her washboard to see another woman descending the stairs, carrying laundry. Lottie's young face is caught in profile with light falling on her elegant neck, a feature which particularly appealed to Orpen. He records with direct honesty and realism a woman whose life is toilsome, but softens this harshness through the delicacy of her neck.

M	T	W	T	F	S	S
1	2	3	4	5	6	7
8	9	10	11	12	13	14
15	16	17	18	19	20	21
22	23	24	25	26	27	28
29	30	31	1	2	3	4

29 Monday · Luan

30 Tuesday · Máirt

31 Wednesday · Céadaoin

1 Thursday · Déardaoin   August · Lúnasa

2 Friday · Aoine

3 Saturday · Satharn

4 Sunday · Domhnach

Gabriel Metsu, *Woman Reading a Letter,* **c.1664–1666**
A lady wearing an ermine-trimmed jacket reads a letter by a window. Her relationship to its sender is suggested by the spaniel, symbolic of fidelity, the bucket decorated with Cupid's arrows and the cast-off shoe, which has erotic connotations in art. The curl on the lady's forehead indicates her engaged status, while a mirror behind her warns against vanity. An abandoned sewing basket and a discarded thimble on the floor suggest that she has forgotten her domestic chores. A maid reveals a picture of a ship in a stormy sea, perhaps a metaphor for romance.

M	T	W	T	F	S	S
1	2	3	4	5	6	7
8	9	10	11	12	13	14
15	16	17	18	19	20	21
22	23	24	25	26	27	28
29	30	31	1	2	3	4

5 Monday · Luan
Bank Holiday

6 Tuesday · Máirt

7 Wednesday · Céadaoin

8 Thursday · Déardaoin

9 Friday · Aoine

10 Saturday · Satharn

11 Sunday · Domhnach

Gabriel Metsu, *Man Writing a Letter,* **c.1664–1666**

A gentleman wearing a black silk suit with a white linen shirt writes a letter at a table covered with an imported Persian carpet. His wide-brimmed hat hangs on the back of a red upholstered chair. The furnishings, silver inkstand and elegant interior suggest this man's affluence. Behind the panes of an open window, a globe signifies his worldly pursuit; he may be a merchant or a learned and well-travelled man. This painting and *Woman Reading a Letter* (previous page) were intended by Metsu as pendants and depict the exchange of a love letter between an Amsterdam couple.

M	T	W	T	F	S	S
29	30	31	1	2	3	4
5	6	7	8	9	10	11
12	13	14	15	16	17	18
19	20	21	22	23	24	25
26	27	28	29	30	31	1

12 Monday · Luan

13 Tuesday · Máirt

14 Wednesday · Céadaoin

15 Thursday · Déardaoin

16 Friday · Aoine

17 Saturday · Satharn

18 Sunday · Domhnach

John Butler Yeats, *Portrait of Jack B. Yeats (1871–1957),* **1890**

This portrait of John Butler Yeats' younger son was painted in London when Jack B. Yeats was an 18- or 19-year-old art student. He wears a grey coat, white shirt and grey-blue bow tie, which complement his fair colouring and blue eyes. His face has been painted quickly, while preserving the transparency of his young skin and rosy cheeks. His coat is painted with broad brushstrokes in different directions and, throughout, the paint appears to be in motion. The slight aura about the head was a feature Yeats developed in later portraits.

M	T	W	T	F	S	S
29	30	31	1	2	3	4
5	6	7	8	9	10	11
12	13	14	15	16	17	18
19	20	21	22	23	24	25
26	27	28	29	30	31	1

August · Lúnasa
Week 34 · Seachtain 34

19 Monday · Luan

20 Tuesday · Máirt

21 Wednesday · Céadaoin

22 Thursday · Déardaoin

23 Friday · Aoine

24 Saturday · Satharn

25 Sunday · Domhnach

Evie Hone, *A Landscape with a Tree,* **1943**

After training in London, Evie Hone studied Cubism in Paris, returning there over many summers. This view of a tree against fields and mountains is typical of the vitality of her later landscapes, in which her ability to capture a sense of place is evident. Hone has turned the background hills into rectangular screens to make a foil for the central grouping of fields and stones against which the central pattern of the tree is shown. This is characteristic of her Expressionist work, showing the influence of Rouault, whom she admired. The treatment of the background, however, betrays earlier Cubist influences.

M	T	W	T	F	S	S
29	30	31	1	2	3	4
5	6	7	8	9	10	11
12	13	14	15	16	17	18
19	20	21	22	23	24	25
26	27	28	29	30	31	1

26 Monday · Luan

27 Tuesday · Máirt

28 Wednesday · Céadaoin

29 Thursday · Déardaoin

30 Friday · Aoine

31 Saturday · Satharn

1 Sunday · Domhnach   September · Meán Fómhair

Jacques-Emile Blanche, *Portrait of James Joyce (1882–1941), Author,* **1934**

While living in Paris, James Joyce was painted twice by Blanche. In this earlier portrait, Joyce sits in an armchair in three-quarter view, turning slightly towards the viewer. This angle was chosen as he was concerned that a frontal pose would accentuate the thick lenses of his spectacles. While the pose and setting are informal, his failing eyesight is nonetheless suggested. Joyce seems uneasy and there is a sense of tension captured in both face and body language. Joyce, never easily pleased, wrote that he thought this portrait was 'awful, except for the splendid tie I had on'.

M	T	W	T	F	S	S
29	30	31	1	2	3	4
5	6	7	8	9	10	11
12	13	14	15	16	17	18
19	20	21	22	23	24	25
26	27	28	29	30	31	1

2 Monday · Luan

3 Tuesday · Máirt

4 Wednesday · Céadaoin

5 Thursday · Déardaoin

6 Friday · Aoine

7 Saturday · Satharn

8 Sunday · Domhnach

Lavinia Fontana, *The Visit of the Queen of Sheba to King Solomon,* **c.1600**

In 1600, the Duke and Duchess of Mantua, Vincenzo I Gonzaga and Eleonora de' Medici, stopped in Bologna, where Fontana painted them, en route to Florence to attend the marriage of Maria de' Medici to Henry IV of France. The Duke and Duchess appear in the guise of King Solomon and the Queen of Sheba. The Queen and her courtiers are attired in lace, brocaded silk, velvet, pearls and rubies. Their sumptuous costumes combine to convey the pomp and ceremony of Italian court life during the career of Fontana, one of the most successful female painters in the history of art.

M	T	W	T	F	S	S
26	27	28	29	30	31	1
2	3	4	5	6	7	8
9	10	11	12	13	14	15
16	17	18	19	20	21	22
23	24	25	26	27	28	29
30	1	2	3	4	5	6

9 Monday • Luan

10 Tuesday • Máirt

11 Wednesday • Céadaoin

12 Thursday • Déardaoin

13 Friday • Aoine

14 Saturday • Satharn

15 Sunday • Domhnach

Matthew William Peters, *Sylvia, A Courtesan,* **c.1778**

Having trained initially in Dublin, Peters travelled to London, Rome and Florence. His versions of Titian's *Venus of Urbino* from the Uffizi earned him the nickname the 'English Titian'. This is a typical example of the mildly erotic works known as 'fancy pictures' which he produced on his return from the continent. They were made available in print form and were popular among a group of English aristocrats with a predilection for slightly risqué subject matter, but they went largely out of fashion after the French Revolution. Peters later regretted painting them, after being ordained an Anglican priest in 1782.

M	T	W	T	F	S	S
26	27	28	29	30	31	1
2	3	4	5	6	7	8
9	10	11	12	13	14	15
16	17	18	19	20	21	22
23	24	25	26	27	28	29
30	1	2	3	4	5	6

September · Meán Fómhair
Week 38 · Seachtain 38

16 Monday · Luan

17 Tuesday · Máirt

18 Wednesday · Céadaoin

19 Thursday · Déardaoin

20 Friday · Aoine

21 Saturday · Satharn

22 Sunday · Domhnach

William Mulready, *The Toy-seller,* **1857–1863**

Born in Ennis, County Clare, Mulready moved to London as a boy and became known for his colourful genre scenes. He was gifted in illustrating subjects with children, who played a central motif in Victorian art. This work belongs to a series of paintings treating the role of mother as educator: she placates her timid child who turns away from a toy seller attempting to attract his attention with a rattle. Their facial expressions, ranging from fear to concern, create a sense of psychological drama. The black toy seller, a rarely treated subject in Victorian art, may represent an exotic presence here.

M	T	W	T	F	S	S
26	27	28	29	30	31	1
2	3	4	5	6	7	8
9	10	11	12	13	14	15
16	17	18	19	20	21	22
23	24	25	26	27	28	29
30	1	2	3	4	5	6

September · Meán Fómhair
Week 39 · Seachtain 39

23 Monday · Luan

24 Tuesday · Máirt

25 Wednesday · Céadaoin

26 Thursday · Déardaoin

27 Friday · Aoine

28 Saturday · Satharn

29 Sunday · Domhnach

John Henry Campbell, *Ringsend and Irishtown from the Grand Canal, Dublin,* **1809**
Campbell was born in England but moved to Dublin while young, establishing himself as a landscape painter. This is an early work, painted in the year he began exhibiting topographical views of Dublin, Wicklow and Killarney. Campbell painted this view when the villages of Ringsend and Irishtown were a unit separated by some distance from the city. A once prosperous fishing community, it remained a quiet, self-contained district situated on a spit of land east of the River Dodder. In the early 19th century a single-arched bridge of mountain granite was erected, reducing the dangers of crossing the Dodder estuary.

M	T	W	T	F	S	S
26	27	28	29	30	31	1
2	3	4	5	6	7	8
9	10	11	12	13	14	15
16	17	18	19	20	21	22
23	24	25	26	27	28	29
30	1	2	3	4	5	6

September · Meán Fómhair
Week 40 · Seachtain 40

30 Monday · Luan

1 Tuesday · Máirt   October · Deireadh Fómhair

2 Wednesday · Céadaoin

3 Thursday · Déardaoin

4 Friday · Aoine

5 Saturday · Satharn

6 Sunday · Domhnach

Willem Cornelisz Duyster, *Portrait of a Married Couple,* **c.1625**

This middle-aged Dutch couple wear, for this date, slightly old-fashioned costume of unadorned but expensive black silk, which is offset against their white neckwear: his, a soft falling linen collar, hers, a starched and pleated cartwheel ruff. Their lace cuffs and the brown fur trim of the lady's dress indicate significant wealth. Equally costly is the imported Persian rug on which the man has placed his wide-brimmed hat. Such carpets were often used as tablecloths in 17th-century Dutch painting. Duyster was based in Amsterdam and his paintings, mainly genre scenes, are comparatively rare, while his portraits are extremely scarce today.

M	T	W	T	F	S	S
26	27	28	29	30	31	1
2	3	4	5	6	7	8
9	10	11	12	13	14	15
16	17	18	19	20	21	22
23	24	25	26	27	28	29
30	1	2	3	4	5	6

October · Deireadh Fómhair
Week 41 · Seachtain 41

7 Monday · Luan

8 Tuesday · Máirt

9 Wednesday · Céadaoin

10 Thursday · Déardaoin

11 Friday · Aoine

12 Saturday · Satharn

13 Sunday · Domhnach

James Sleator, *Self-Portrait,* **c.1915**

From County Armagh, Sleator trained at the Belfast School of Art, where he won a scholarship to the Metropolitan School of Art in Dublin. His professor there was William Orpen. Sleator completed his training at the Slade in London and in Paris, returning to Dublin in 1915. It was around this date that he painted this striking self-portrait, which demonstrates Sleator's indebtedness to his mentor Orpen, like whom, he enjoyed portraying himself. This work was described in *The Studio* magazine in 1915 as 'full of distinction and beauty of tone'. In London, Sleator established himself as a successful portraitist.

M	T	W	T	F	S	S
30	1	2	3	4	5	6
7	8	9	10	11	12	13
14	15	16	17	18	19	20
21	22	23	24	25	26	27
28	29	30	31	1	2	3

October • Deireadh Fómhair

Week 42 • Seachtain 42

14 Monday • Luan

15 Tuesday • Máirt

16 Wednesday • Céadaoin

17 Thursday • Déardaoin

18 Friday • Aoine

19 Saturday • Satharn

20 Sunday • Domhnach

Helen Mabel Trevor, Interior of a Breton Cottage, **1892**

Helen Mabel Trevor was born in County Down and studied art in London and Paris. She was a frequent visitor to Brittany in the 1880s and 1890s, becoming known for her scenes of Breton women in their homes, which she painted with an increasingly strong sense of realism. Here, Trevor depicts the sparsely furnished interior of a cottage where an old woman is absorbed in her daily task of peeling potatoes. The humble subject matter is captured in thin brushstrokes of predominantly brown tones, relieved only by the shaft of light entering through partially opened shutters.

M	T	W	T	F	S	S
30	1	2	3	4	5	6
7	8	9	10	11	12	13
14	15	16	17	18	19	20
21	22	23	24	25	26	27
28	29	30	31	1	2	3

Helen Mabel Trevor 1892

October · Deireadh Fómhair
Week 43 · Seachtain 43

21 Monday · Luan

22 Tuesday · Máirt

23 Wednesday · Céadaoin

24 Thursday · Déardaoin

25 Friday · Aoine

26 Saturday · Satharn

27 Sunday · Domhnach

Nicholas Joseph Crowley, *Invitation, Hesitation, Persuasion,* **1846**

Young women appear to arrive at a social event, possibly a fancy dress party of the kind popular in Britain and Ireland in the mid-19th century. Queen Victoria and Prince Albert popularised fancy dress as an alternative to the usual formality of upper-class entertainment by participating in *bals costumés* at Buckingham Palace in 1842, 1845 and 1851. The second of these balls had a mid-18th-century theme. Revival fancy dress was already a well-established practice, with revellers dressing in their ancestors' clothes. These women's 18th-century floral silk gowns may have been retrieved from family attics and re-modelled for such an occasion.

M	T	W	T	F	S	S
30	1	2	3	4	5	6
7	8	9	10	11	12	13
14	15	16	17	18	19	20
21	22	23	24	25	26	27
28	29	30	31	1	2	3

October · Deireadh Fómhair
Week 44 · Seachtain 44

28 Monday · Luan
Bank Holiday (RoI)

29 Tuesday · Máirt

30 Wednesday · Céadaoin

31 Thursday · Déardaoin

1 Friday · Aoine   November · Samhain

2 Saturday · Satharn

3 Sunday · Domhnach

Nathaniel Hone the Younger, *View of the Coast, County Clare,* **1890s**

Having spent 17 years in France painting *en plein air*, Hone returned to Ireland. His fascination with the sea reached a climax in the 1890s when he created a series of paintings of the dramatic rocky coast around Kilkee, County Clare. These pictures reveal Hone's skills as a painter of elemental nature – land, sea, sky, breaking waves, changing light and weather conditions. In order to capture these transient effects, Hone painted rapidly, using vigorous brushstrokes and a thick application of paint, showing the influence of Gustave Courbet, the Barbizon and Impressionist painters whom he had studied in France.

M	T	W	T	F	S	S
30	1	2	3	4	5	6
7	8	9	10	11	12	13
14	15	16	17	18	19	20
21	22	23	24	25	26	27
28	29	30	31	1	2	3

4 Monday · Luan

5 Tuesday · Máirt

6 Wednesday · Céadaoin

7 Thursday · Déardaoin

8 Friday · Aoine

9 Saturday · Satharn

10 Sunday · Domhnach

Sarah Paxton Ball Dodson, *Mayfield Convent,* **late 19th century**

Born in Philadelphia, Dodson studied at the Pennsylvania Academy of Fine Arts before travelling to Paris and becoming a leading American woman artist there in the late 19th century. In 1891 she left France and moved to Brighton, England, where her brother lived. Sarah turned increasingly to painting landscapes such as this, which depicts Mayfield Convent in East Sussex across a lake and through a screen of delicate trees. Mayfield, originally a medieval bishop's palace, was restored in the 19th century by E.W. Pugin and converted into a convent incorporating a girls' school, with a progressive educational philosophy for the time.

M	T	W	T	F	S	S
28	29	30	31	1	2	3
4	5	6	7	8	9	10
11	12	13	14	15	16	17
18	19	20	21	22	23	24
25	26	27	28	29	30	1

November · Samhain
Week 46 · Seachtain 46

11 Monday · Luan

12 Tuesday · Máirt

13 Wednesday · Céadaoin

14 Thursday · Déardaoin

15 Friday · Aoine

16 Saturday · Satharn

17 Sunday · Domhnach

Unknown Artist, *Portrait of a Woman Aged Twenty-Two,* **1567**
This young lady wears an embroidered dress with lightly puffed shoulders, a raised collar, thin gold chains and white sleeves with black embroidered wristbands. Her portrait may have been intended to hang beside one of her husband: her married status is shown by her jewelled headdress and the rings on her fingers. The coat-of-arms behind her remains unidentified due to paint loss. Suspended from a gold chain around her neck is a heart-shaped medallion with Christ on the Cross. Martin Luther adopted a similar motif for his coat-of-arms, so the medallion may reflect the woman's affiliations to the Lutheran church.

M	T	W	T	F	S	S
28	29	30	31	1	2	3
4	5	6	7	8	9	10
11	12	13	14	15	16	17
18	19	20	21	22	23	24
25	26	27	28	29	30	1

1·5·6·7

ÆTATISSVÆZ

18 Monday · Luan

19 Tuesday · Máirt

20 Wednesday · Céadaoin

21 Thursday · Déardaoin

22 Friday · Aoine

23 Saturday · Satharn

24 Sunday · Domhnach

Edwin Henry Landseer, *A King Charles Spaniel,* **1840s**

Landseer was Queen Victoria's favourite painter. He specialised in portraying animals in a somewhat sentimental light and often gave them semi-human expressions, which secured his popularity during an era when sensibilities were all-important. The spaniel's round face and eyes are echoed in the circular format of the picture, while its gentle, innocent expression epitomises the popular image of such a domestic animal, that of complete devotion to its master.

M	T	W	T	F	S	S
28	29	30	31	1	2	3
4	5	6	7	8	9	10
11	12	13	14	15	16	17
18	19	20	21	22	23	24
25	26	27	28	29	30	1

25 Monday · Luan

26 Tuesday · Máirt

27 Wednesday · Céadaoin

28 Thursday · Déardaoin

29 Friday · Aoine

30 Saturday · Satharn

1 Sunday · Domhnach   December · Nollaig

George Sharp, *Repose,* **1867**

Born in Dublin, Sharp trained in Paris and came under the influence of French Realism, perhaps the first Irish artist to do so. On his return to Ireland, he painted portraits and genre subjects, often including downtrodden or marginal figures in society. The model for this elderly man, a turf carrier, appears in at least one other work by Sharp. He sits with eyes closed and hands clasped, his face, clothing and battered boots rendered in broad, sweeping brushstrokes. His red cravat contrasts with the earthy tones elsewhere. Bright light falls upon his forehead and the earthenware jug, casting dark shadows.

M	T	W	T	F	S	S
28	29	30	31	1	2	3
4	5	6	7	8	9	10
11	12	13	14	15	16	17
18	19	20	21	22	23	24
25	26	27	28	29	30	1

2 Monday · Luan

3 Tuesday · Máirt

4 Wednesday · Céadaoin

5 Thursday · Déardaoin

6 Friday · Aoine

7 Saturday · Satharn

8 Sunday · Domhnach

Harry Clarke, *The Snow Queen,* **c.1916**

Employing vivid colours in ink and watercolour, Clarke presents Hans Christian Andersen's *Snow Queen* as a radiant, statuesque and hieratic beauty. Elaborately costumed in a jewelled crown and intricately patterned cloak, she emanates a chilling cold, echoing Andersen's words: 'She was beautiful and delicate, but of ice – of shining, glittering ice. Yet she was alive; her eyes flashed like two clear stars, but there was no peace or rest in them.' Kay, bewitched by the Snow Queen and imprisoned in her ice palace, holds a sled and wears a plumed shako hat, ruby red shawl, gloves and pom-pommed shoes.

M	T	W	T	F	S	S
25	26	27	28	29	30	1
2	3	4	5	6	7	8
9	10	11	12	13	14	15
16	17	18	19	20	21	22
23	24	25	26	27	28	29
30	31	1	2	3	4	5

December · Nollaig
Week 50 · Seachtain 50

9 Monday · Luan

10 Tuesday · Máirt

11 Wednesday · Céadaoin

12 Thursday · Déardaoin

13 Friday · Aoine

14 Saturday · Satharn

15 Sunday · Domhnach

Daniel Maclise, *Merry Christmas in the Baron's Hall,* **1838**

In the interior of a large Jacobean hall, Christmas is celebrated with festivity and abandon. A boar's head, decorated with bay and rosemary, is served on a silver platter while the Lord of Misrule chants a carol in its praise. Father Christmas mixes the wassails (spiced ale or mulled wine) while Saint Distaff hands him the roasted pippins that will be served with them. Also enjoying the banquet are Saint George and the dragon, a Turk, a jester on a hobby horse, a juggler, a fiddler and numerous choristers, musicians and revellers.

M	T	W	T	F	S	S
25	26	27	28	29	30	1
2	3	4	5	6	7	8
9	10	11	12	13	14	15
16	17	18	19	20	21	22
23	24	25	26	27	28	29
30	31	1	2	3	4	5

December · Nollaig
Week 51 · Seachtain 51

16 Monday · Luan

17 Tuesday · Máirt

18 Wednesday · Céadaoin

19 Thursday · Déardaoin

20 Friday · Aoine

21 Saturday · Satharn

22 Sunday · Domhnach

Jean-Antoine Watteau, *Woman Seen from the Back,* **c.1715–1716**

Watteau is regarded as one of the greatest draughtsmen in the history of European art. He was a master of the technique known as *aux trois crayons,* a combination of red, black and white chalks. Most of Watteau's drawings are figure studies. He was particularly intrigued by figures seen from the back. They occur frequently in his work, often as solitary figures detached from the main group, as in this beautiful drawing of a woman.

M	T	W	T	F	S	S
25	26	27	28	29	30	1
2	3	4	5	6	7	8
9	10	11	12	13	14	15
16	17	18	19	20	21	22
23	24	25	26	27	28	29
30	31	1	2	3	4	5

23 Monday · Luan

24 Tuesday · Máirt
Christmas Eve

25 Wednesday · Céadaoin
Christmas Day

26 Thursday · Déardaoin
St Stephen's Day

27 Friday · Aoine

28 Saturday · Satharn

29 Sunday · Domhnach

Style of Pieter Coecke van Aelst, *The Adoration of the Magi,* **mid-16th century**

After training in Aelst, Coecke spent some time in Rome and translated and edited the architectural treatises of Serlio and Vitruvius. Coecke was multi-talented, designing tapestries, chariots and triumphal arches for Charles V and his son Philip, stained-glass windows for Antwerp Cathedral and decoration for the town hall. Among his pupils were Willem Key and Pieter Brueghel the Elder. He had a significant influence on 16th-century Flemish painting and attracted many followers, including the author of this panel. The classical *contrapposto* positions of the Christ Child and the magus on the right reveal an Italian Raphaelesque or Mannerist influence.

M	T	W	T	F	S	S
25	26	27	28	29	30	1
2	3	4	5	6	7	8
9	10	11	12	13	14	15
16	17	18	19	20	21	22
23	24	25	26	27	28	29
30	31	1	2	3	4	5

December · Nollaig
Week 1 · Seachtain 1

30 Monday · Luan

31 Tuesday · Máirt
New Year's Eve

1 Wednesday · Céadaoin
New Year's Day

2020 January · Eanáir

2 Thursday · Déardaoin

3 Friday · Aoine

4 Saturday · Satharn

5 Sunday · Domhnach

Nicolaes Molenaer, *A Winter Scene,* **17th century**
Unlike many Dutch winter scenes, this painting does not show skaters enjoying themselves on the ice, but depicts people going about their business. The buildings on the right are possibly intended as the walls of Molenaer's native Haarlem. On the extreme right is an inn; the wreath hanging from the pole above the door indicates that refreshments were available there. A horse-drawn sledge carries fodder for animals and other figures push sledges across the ice. Molenaer repeated this type of composition with some variation in many river or winter landscapes, which reveal the influence of van Ruisdael and van Ostade.

M	T	W	T	F	S	S
25	26	27	28	29	30	1
2	3	4	5	6	7	8
9	10	11	12	13	14	15
16	17	18	19	20	21	22
23	24	25	26	27	28	29
30	31	1	2	3	4	5

List of Works

All images Photo © National Gallery of Ireland unless otherwise stated.

Richard Cosway, English, 1742–1821 *Self-Portrait in Elizabethan Costume; A Lock of His Hair (on verso),* c.1790 Watercolour on ivory, 7.1 x 5.7 cm, NGI.3024,

Harry Clarke, Irish, 1889–1931, *The Swineherd,* Ink, graphite, watercolour gouache and glazes with bodycolour highlights on paper, 36 x 24.8 cm, NGI.2008.89.7

Gareth Reid, Irish, 21st Century, *Graham Norton (born Dublin 1963), Broadcaster, Comedian, Actor and Writer,* Oil on canvas, 2017, 137 x 107cm, Winner's commission from Sky Arts *Portrait Artist of the Year 2017.* Presented, Storyvault Films, 2017, NGI 2017.7

Joseph Mallord William Turner, English, 1775–1851, *A Ship against the Mewstone, at the Entrance to Plymouth Sound,* c.1814, Watercolour with white highlights and scraping-out on cream wove card, 15.6 x 23.7 cm, NGI.2413

Christian Adolf Schreyer, German, 1828–1899, *Arab Horsemen,* 1865/1885, Oil on canvas, 57 x 69 cm, NGI.4275

Howard Helmick, American, 1840–1907, *News of the Land League,* 1881, Oil on canvas, 80.5 x 105 cm, NGI.4507

Frans Hals, Dutch, c.1581–1666, *A Fisherboy,* c.1630, Oil on canvas, 74.1 x 60 cm, NGI.193

Robert Ponsonby Staples, Irish, 1853–1943, *On the Beach, Broadstairs, Kent,* 1899, Oil on canvas, NGI.4712

Sarah Cecilia Harrison, Irish, 1863–1941, *Self-Portrait,* Oil on canvas, 37 x 27 cm, NGI.1279

Frederic William Burton, Irish, 1816–1900, *Hellelil and Hildebrand, the Meeting on the Turret Stairs,* 1864, Watercolour and gouache on paper, 95.5 x 60.8 cm, NGI.2358

Richard Rothwell, Irish, 1800–1868, *Calisto,* c.1840, Oil on canvas, 89 x 112 cm, NGI.506

Howard Helmick, American, 1840–1907, *The Bookworm,* 19th century, Oil on canvas, 45 x 54 cm, NGI.4294

Gabriele Münter, German, 1877–1962, *Girl with a Red Ribbon,* 1908, Oil on board, 40.7 x 32.8 cm © Estate of Gabriele Münter, VG Bild-Kunst, Bonn/IVARO, Dublin 2018, NGI.2006.12

John Lavery, Irish, 1856–1941, *Saint Patrick's Purgatory, Lough Derg,* Oil on canvas on board, 60.5 x 50.5 cm, NGI.4666

Roderic O'Conor (1860–1940) *Bretonne,* c.1903–1904, Oil on canvas, Unframed: 54.5 x 45.6 cm, NGI.4571

Michelangelo Merisi da Caravaggio, Italian, 1571–1610, *The Taking of Christ,* 1602, Oil on canvas, 135.5 x 169.5 cm, On indefinite loan to the National Gallery of Ireland from the Jesuit Community, Leeson St., Dublin, who acknowledge the kind generosity of the late Dr Marie Lea-Wilson, L.14702

Colin Middleton, Irish, 1910–1983, *Landscape in May, Carnmoney,* 1943, Oil on canvas, 51 x 61 cm, © Estate of Colin Middleton, IVARO, Dublin 2018, NGI.4667

William Evans of Eton, English, 1798–1877, *Interior with a Woman Spinning, a Pot on an Open Fire,* 1838, Watercolour and graphite on paper, 43 x 58 cm, NGI.2008.36.12

Stanley Royle, British, 1888–1961, *The Goose Girl,* c.1921, Oil on canvas, 72 x 91 cm © The Artist's Estate. All Rights Reserved 2018/ Bridgeman Art Library, NGI.4009

Bernardo Strozzi, Italian, 1581–1644, *Allegory of Spring and Summer,* late 1630s, Oil on canvas, 72 x 128 cm, NGI.856

After Jean-Baptiste Greuze, French, 1725–1805, *The Capuchin Doll,* Oil on canvas, 43 x 37 cm, NGI.803

John Butler Yeats, Irish, 1839–1922, *Pippa Passes (illustration for Browning's poem of 1841),* 1869/1871, Gouache on paper, 48.4 x 34.6 cm, NGI.3531

Melchior de Hondecoeter, Dutch, 1636–1695, *Poultry,* 1660s-90s, Oil on canvas, 101.5 x 130 cm, NGI.509

Vincent Van Gogh, Dutch, (1853–1890), *Rooftops in Paris,* 1886, Oil on canvas, 45.6 x 38.5 cm, NGI.2007.2

Richard Rothwell, Irish, 1800–1868, *A Study from Nature - Glendalough - Guides to the Churches on the Look-out for Tourists' Baskets,* Oil on panel, 108 x 150 cm, NGI.4331

James Humbert Craig, Irish, 1877–1944, *Cushendun in June,* Oil on board, 51 x 61 cm, NGI.4593

William John Leech, Irish, 1881–1968, *A Convent Garden, Brittany,* c.1913, Oil on canvas, 132 x 106 cm, © National Gallery of Ireland, NGI.1245

William Orpen, Irish, 1878–1931, *Looking at the Sea,* 1912, Oil on panel, 61 x 50 cm, NGI.956

Chäim Soutine, Russian, 1893–1943, *Landscape with Flight of Stairs,* c.1922, Oil on canvas, 81.5 x 65 cm, NGI.4485

Mary Swanzy, Irish, 1882–1978, *Clown by Candlelight,* 1942–1943, Oil on wood, 14 x 19 cm, © The Artist's Estate, NGI.1415

William Crozier, Irish, 1930–2011, *The Re-planting,* 2008, Carborundum: Sheet: 49.5 x 64.3 cm, Plate: 39.5 x 54.3 cm © The Artist's Estate, NGI.2008.23

Walter Frederick Osborne, Irish, 1859–1903, *Dublin Streets: A Vendor of Books,* 1889, Oil on canvas, 80 x 90 cm, NGI.4736

William Orpen, Irish, 1878–1931, *The Wash House,* 1905, Oil on canvas, 91 x 73 cm, NGI.946

Gabriel Metsu, Dutch, 1629–1667, *Woman Reading a Letter,* 1664–1666, Oil on wood panel, 52.5 x 40.2 cm, Presented, Sir Alfred and Lady Beit, 1987 (Beit Collection), NGI.4537

Gabriel Metsu, Dutch, 1629–1667, *Man Writing a Letter,* 1664–1666, Oil on wood panel, 52.5 x 40.2 cm, Presented, Sir Alfred and Lady Beit, 1987 (Beit Collection), NGI.4536

John Butler Yeats, Irish, 1839–1922, *Portrait of Jack B. Yeats (1871–1957),* 1890, Oil on canvas, 61 x 51 cm, NGI.4040

Evie Hone, Irish, 1894–1955, *A Landscape with a Tree,* 1943, Oil on board, 69 x 69 cm, Reproduced with permission from the Friends of the National Collections of Ireland, © The Artist's Estate, NGI.4322

Jacques-Emile Blanche, French, 1861–1942, *Portrait of James Joyce (1882–1941), Author,* 1934, Oil on canvas, 82 x 65 cm, NGI.1051

Lavinia Fontana, Italian, 1552–1614, *The Visit of the Queen of Sheba to King Solomon,* c.1600, Oil on canvas, 256 x 325 cm, NGI.76

Matthew William Peters, English, 1742–1814, *Sylvia, a Courtesan,* c.1778, Oil on panel, 63 x 76 cm, NGI.4049

William Mulready, Irish, 1786–1863, *The Toy-seller,* 1857–1863, Oil on canvas, 112 x 142 cm, NGI.387

John Henry Campbell, Irish, 1757–1829, *Ringsend and Irishtown from the Grand Canal,* Dublin, 1809, Watercolour on paper, 44.6 x 56.5 cm, NGI.3970

Willem Cornelisz Duyster, Dutch, 1599–1635, *Portrait of a Married Couple,* Oil on wood panel, 64.2 x 51.5 cm, NGI.556

James Sleator, Northern Irish, 1885–1950, *Self-Portrait,* c.1915, Oil on canvas, 89.5 x 63.5 cm, © The Artist's Estate, NGI.4493

Helen Mabel Trevor, Irish, 1831–1900, *An Interior of a Breton Cottage,* 1892, Oil on canvas, 63 x 46 cm, NGI.501

Nicholas Joseph Crowley, Irish, 1813–1857, *Invitation, Hesitation and Persuasion,* c.1846, Oil on canvas, 102 x 127 cm, NGI.4330

Nathaniel Hone the Younger, Irish, 1831–1917, *View of the Coast,* County Clare, Oil on canvas, 61 x 92 cm, NGI.1442

Sarah Paxton Ball Dodson, American, 1847–1906, *Mayfield Convent,* 19th century, Oil on canvas, 35.5 x 44.5 cm, NGI.4000

Unknown Artist, German (Upper Saxony), 16th century, German, *Portrait of a Woman Aged Twenty-Two,* 1567, Oil on limewood panel, 63 x 46.4 cm, NGI.974

Edwin Henry Landseer, English, 1802–1873, *A King Charles Spaniel,* 1845, Oil on canvas, 35 x 35 cm, NGI.4333

George Sharp, Irish, 1802–1877, *Repose,* 1867, Oil on canvas, 51 x 42 cm, NGI.85

Harry Clarke, Irish, 1889–1931, *The Snow Queen,* Ink, graphite, watercolour, gouache and glazes, with bodycolour highlights, 40 x 28.2 cm, NGI.2008.89.2

Daniel Maclise, Irish, 1806–1870, *Merry Christmas in the Baron's Hall,* 1838, Oil on canvas, 183 x 366 cm, NGI.156

Jean-Antoine Watteau, French, 1684-1721, *Woman Seen from the Back,* c.1715/1716, Graphite and red chalk on paper, 14 x 9.6 cm, NGI.2299

Style of Pieter Coecke van Aelst, Flemish, 1502–1550, *The Adoration of the Magi,* mid-16th century, Oil on oak panel, 65.4 x 48.4 cm, NGI.361

Nicolaes Molenaer, Dutch, 1628/29–1676, *A Winter Scene,* Oil on panel, 47 x 62.6 cm, NGI.682

FRONT COVER
AE [George William Russell], Irish, 1867–1935, *Portrait of Iseult Gonne (Mrs Francis Stuart),* Oil on canvas, 56 x 46 cm, NGI.1787

BACK COVER
Mainie Jellett, Irish, 1897–1944, *The Virgin and Child,* 1936, Gouache and graphite on paper, 27.5 x 20 cm, NGI.7840

ENDPAPERS
John Faulkner, Irish, 1835–1894, *Inniskea Isle, Achill,* Watercolour and graphite on paper, Sheet: 47.7 x 81.2 cm, NGI.2011.6